Contents

Icons used in this book

This 'pointer' icon marks the brief introduction that sets the piece of writing in context and provides useful background information.

This 'be safe' icon marks important information relating to the use of the text – including personal safety.

This icon indicates that it would be useful for you to have access to a dictionary.

Spider in the bath

Sometimes we are afraid of things for no good reason. They cannot harm us, yet still they frighten us. The speaker in this poem is not squeamish, but has one great, irrational fear.

I've picked up frogs,
And patted dogs,
Stroked the skin of snakes.
I've tickled cats,
Examined bats,
Fed the ducks and drakes.

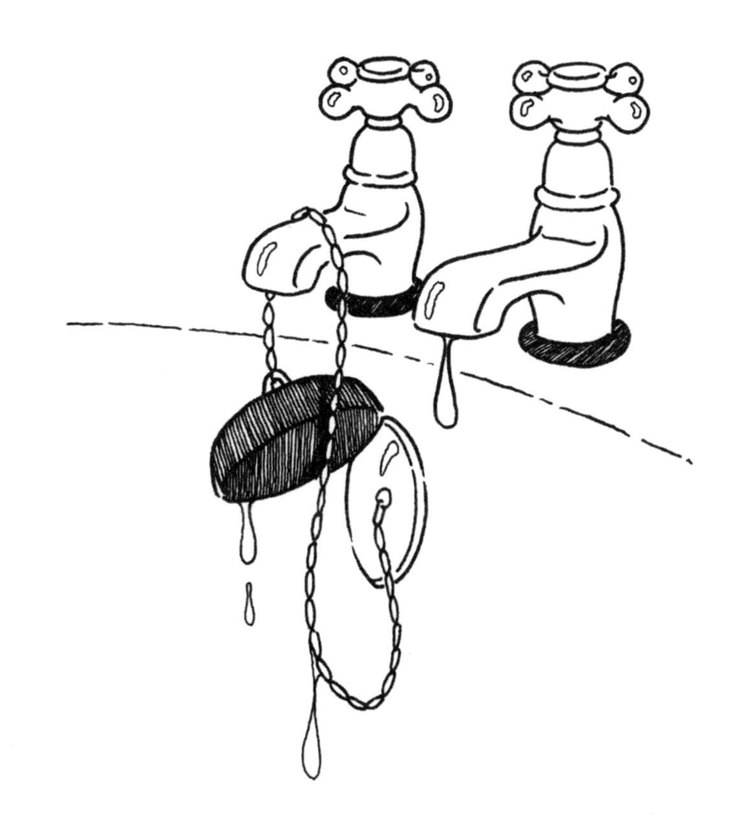

I've chased fat hens,
Pushed sheep in pens,
Held chickens in my hand.
Been stung by bees
On both my knees,
Pulled crabs out of the sand.

I've watched a mole
Go down his hole,
Followed ants along a path.
So why am I
So frightened of
A spider in the bath?

Lynette Craig

Part 1

1 a) In the first verse, what does the speaker look at most closely?

_______________ 1 mark

b) Which word in the poem helped you to answer? _______________ 1 mark

2 In verse 2, which action is **being done to** the person speaking?

(Explain what is happening and where.)

_______________ 2 marks

3 a) Imagine that the poet writes another verse to this poem. It begins:

I've cuddled slugs / and played with . . .

Which word would fit to finish these two lines? (ring **one**) 1 mark

snails bugs worms mice

b) Explain why you chose this word. _______________ 1 mark

Part 2

4 Which creatures has the speaker tickled?

_______________ 1 mark

5 What has the speaker done to sheep?

_______________ 1 mark

6 a) Name **one** creature in the poem that lives or hides underground.

_______________ 1 mark

b) Which words tell you that it lives or hides underground?

_______________ 1 mark

7 Look at these drawings. Colour the **two** animals that are in the poem.

2 marks

page 5
total out of 12

Stars twinkle

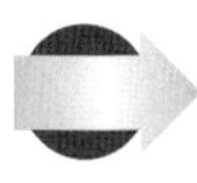

Gazing at the millions of stars in the night sky is exciting and can make us feel very small. This text begins to answer some of our questions about the galaxy and the universe.

How many stars are there?

There are about 1000 billion stars in the Milky Way. That's nearly 200 stars for every person living on Earth today!

Although we can't see all of it, astronomers have worked out how big the universe is and how many stars it has. There are about 100 billion billion stars, in around 100 billion galaxies. It's hard even to think about so many stars, let alone count them!

What are stars made of?

Stars aren't solid like the ground beneath your feet. Instead, they are made of gases like the air around you. The two main gases in stars are hydrogen and helium. They are the stars' fuel. Stars make heat and light from them.

Why do stars twinkle?

Stars only twinkle when we look at them from Earth. Out in space their light shines steadily. We see them twinkling and shimmering because of the air around the Earth – as light from a star travels towards us, it is bent and wobbled by bubbles of hot and cold air.

Are stars star-shaped?

No, stars are round, like balls. We give them pointy edges when we draw them because this is what they look like from Earth, with their light blinking and twinkling.

From *I Wonder Why Stars Twinkle?*
Carole Stott

Glossary

astronomers scientists who study stars and planets
galaxy (plural: galaxies) group(s) of stars in space – each is like a gigantic star-city
Milky Way the name of the galaxy in which our planet Earth is located
universe the whole world and everything beyond it

Part 1

1. If all the stars in our galaxy could be shared out among all the people alive on Earth today, how many stars would each person have? Write your answer in words.

____________________ 1 mark

2. The Milky Way is the __________ of stars and planets that includes our planet Earth. 1 mark

3. What do astronomers do?

____________________ 1 mark

4. What are the **two** main gases that stars are made of?

____________________ 2 marks

5. Where would we need to be to see a star's light shining steadily?

____________________ 1 mark

Part 2

6. Which word in the text means almost the same as 'twinkling'?

____________________ 1 mark

7. a) Draw a star as it appears when you look up at the night sky.

1 mark

b) Why do stars seem to have points when we look at them from Earth?

____

____________________ 1 mark

8. What shape are stars really? ____________________ 1 mark

page 7
total out of 10

The Iron Man returns

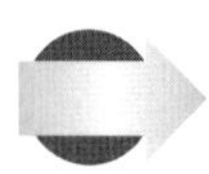

This text comes from a science fiction story that is sometimes described as a modern fairy tale. A country boy called Hogarth has spotted two green lights on the top of a cliff.

Then, as Hogarth watched, a huge dark figure climbed up over the cliff-top. The two lights rose into the sky. They were the giant figure's eyes. A giant black figure, taller than a house, black and towering in the twilight, with green headlamp eyes. The Iron Man! There he stood on the cliff-top, looking inland.
Hogarth began to run. He ran and ran. Home. Home.
The Iron Man had come back.

So he got home at last and gasping for breath he told his dad. An Iron Man! An Iron Man! A giant!

His father frowned. His mother grew pale. His little sister began to cry.

His father took down his double-barrelled gun. He believed his son. He went out. He locked the door. He got in his car. He drove to the next farm.

But that farmer laughed. He was a fat, red man, with a fat, red-mouthed laugh. When he stopped laughing, his eyes were red too. An Iron Man? Nonsense, he said.

So Hogarth's father got back in his car. Now it was dark and it had begun to rain. He drove to the next farm.

The farmer frowned. He believed. Tomorrow, he said, we must see what he is, this iron man. His feet will have left tracks in the earth.

So Hogarth's father again got back into his car. But as he turned the car in the yard, he saw a strange thing in the headlamps. Half a tractor lay there, just half, chopped clean off, the other half missing. He got out of his car and the other farmer came to look too. The tractor had been bitten off – there were big teeth-marks in the steel.

From *The Iron Man*
Ted Hughes (1930–1998)

Part 1

1. Where are these events taking place? ______________________ 1 mark

2. Give **two** words that the author uses to describe the giant's eyes.

   ______________________ 2 marks

3. Why do you think the author repeats the words 'ran' and 'Home'?

   ______________________ 1 mark

4. Hogarth's family turn pale and cry when they hear about the Iron Man.

   a) What does this tell us of their feelings about the Iron Man?

   ______________________ 1 mark

   b) What does this suggest about what the Iron Man is like?

   ______________________ 1 mark

Part 2

5. a) What do you think the father had in mind when he left the house?

   ______________________ 1 mark

   b) Why did he lock the door?

   ______________________ 1 mark

6. Hogarth's father visits two farmers who live nearby. They each react differently to the news of an 'Iron Man'. Explain how each farmer reacts.

   ____

   ______________________ 2 marks

7. The next day, how will the men find where the Iron Man has gone?

   ______________________ 1 mark

8. What can we guess from the big teeth marks in the tractor?

   ______________________ 1 mark

page 9
total out of 12

One-eyed monster

As Odysseus and his men are sailing from Ithaca, their ship runs aground on an island. When they explore the island, they find that it is inhabited by the one-eyed monster, Cyclops. The scene below takes place in Cyclops's cave, where the men have found something to eat.

Cyclops: *(in a clumsy attempt at cunning)*
So, er, where did Ithaca men land them ship?

Polites: *(whispering)*
Don't tell him. He'll find it and crush it.

Eurylochys: Odysseus, throw him off the scent.

Odysseus: Our ship was wrecked.
We entered the bay.
We swam for our lives.
Myself and the men that you see are all that's left.

Cyclops mumbles and muses to himself, then giggles, then mumbles and giggles some more.

Cyclops: Cyclops lonely. Cyclops on his own.

Elpenos: Aw, look at him, he's just a big kid.

Eurybates: He's grinning. You're right. He's a big soft lump really.

Cyclops giggles and laughs. The men begin to laugh.

Antiphus: He likes us. He thinks we are his friends – big dumb animal. Come on, let's help ourselves to this fodder.

Odysseus: Wait a second, let me talk to him some more.

Antiphus: It's fine. Hey, one-eye, how about me and you get our teeth stuck into that slab of cheese over there? I'll have the first bite . . .

Cyclops grabs the man and devours him. The other men scream and shout as Antiphus is crushed and eaten. Cyclops slabbers and drools and burps as he gobbles his victim, crunching his bones between his teeth.

Odysseus: Everyone, get right back into the crag where he can't reach us.

Polites: He's closing the door – we're trapped.

From *Homer's Odyssey*
Simon Armitage

Part 1

1. Complete this sentence. 1 mark

   When a ship has drifted into water too shallow for sailing, it has 'run ________________'.

2. What does 'throw him off the scent' mean? (ring **one**)

   don't let him sniff you　　do something to mislead him
   throw him to the ground 1 mark

3. Why don't Odysseus's men want to tell Cyclops where their ship is?

   ____ 1 mark

4. What do the men think about Cyclops when he starts mumbling and grinning to himself?

   ____ 1 mark

5. In this playscript, some sentences are written in *italics*. What is the purpose of these words?

   ____ 1 mark

Part 2

6. What does Antiphus mean when he says, 'let's help ourselves to this **fodder**'?

   ____ 1 mark

7. Why doesn't Antiphus listen to Odysseus when he tells him to wait? Give **two** reasons.

   ____

   ____ 2 marks

8. What name does Antiphus call Cyclops? ________________ 1 mark

9. How do we know that Odysseus was right not to trust Cyclops?

   ____ 1 mark

page 11
total out of 10

Swede pulls up carrot 'wearing' her long lost wedding ring

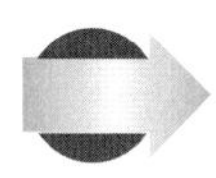

Have you ever lost something that is important to you? You always hope that you will find it again. Sometimes you have to wait a long time – and lost items can turn up in the strangest places.

A Swedish woman pulled up a carrot from her vegetable patch only to discover it was 'wearing' the wedding ring she had lost in 1995.

Lena Pahlsson, from Sweden, had given up on ever finding the white gold ring after it went missing from her kitchen counter 17 years ago.

At the time Lena and her husband Ola had searched frantically for the ring, checking behind appliances and beneath the floor boards before finally giving up.

But as Lena was pulling up the last of this year's carrots she noticed that one had something attached to it.

Husband Ola told the local newspaper: "Our daughter Anna was at home at the time and she heard an almighty scream from the garden."

At first Anna thought her mother had hurt herself and rushed out to help. She instead found Lena sitting on a chair looking rather shocked.

Ola added: "It was Lena's wedding ring that had been missing since 1995 after Lena's annual Christmas baking. It had surfaced, wrapped around a carrot. Quite amazing."

The family have now come up with a theory as to how the ring could have ended up attached to a carrot. They believe their sheep, which is often fed kitchen scraps, somehow gobbled it up and its manure was spread over the vegetable patch.

Unfortunately Lena hasn't been able to wear the ring again yet, as her fingers have grown over the last 17 years so it now needs to be re-sized to fit properly.

She said: "We're keeping it in a safe place."

From the *Daily Mail*, 1 January 2012

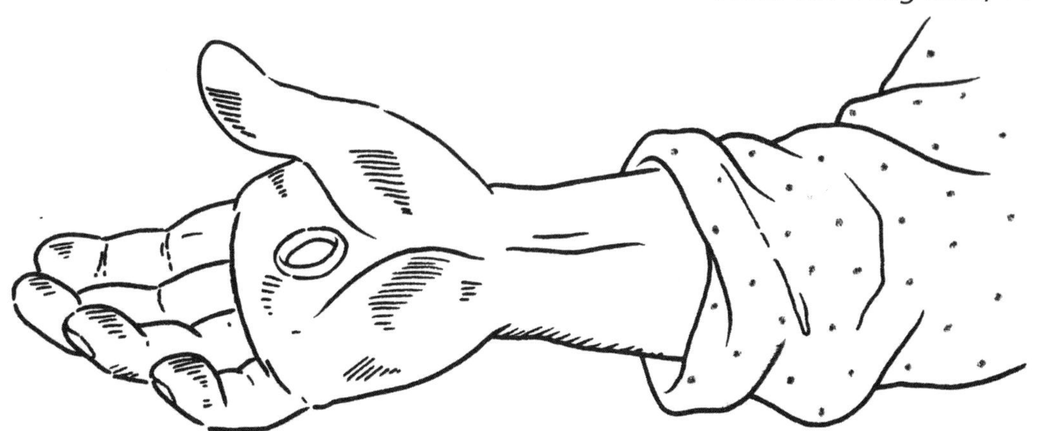

Part 1

1. The author has fun with words in the title. Swedes and carrots are both vegetables, but a Swede is also a person who lives in (ring **one**):

   the South West   Switzerland   Sweden   Swaziland.   1 mark

2. In the subtitle, the writer makes the carrot sound like a person. Write the word that suggests this. ______________________   1 mark

3. What is Lena's husband's first name? ______________________   1 mark

4. What had Lena been doing when the ring went missing? (ring **one**)

   cleaning   baking   washing up   gardening   1 mark

5. At what time of year did the ring go missing?

   ______________________   1 mark

6. When her ring went missing, where did Lena look for it? (ring **two**)

   under the floor boards   in the bin
   behind things in the kitchen   down the back of the sofa   2 marks

Part 2

7. Who is Anna? ______________________   1 mark

8. When Anna hears a scream, what does she think has happened?

   ______________________   1 mark

9. Lena's family think they know how the ring ended up around a carrot. Fill in the gaps to explain what they think happened.

   The ring fell into kitchen scraps, which were fed to the ____________ . The animal's droppings, including the ring, were spread as manure on the ____________ patch.   2 marks

10. Why does the ring no longer fit Lena when she finally finds it?

    ______________________   1 mark

page 13
total out of 12

Mary and the robin

'Mistress Mary' is 10 years old and has recently arrived in England from India. She is a lonely little girl and an orphan who has never been to school. When she hears about a secret garden, she is determined to find it.

"Oh!" she cried out, "is it you – is it you?" And it did not seem at all queer to her that she spoke to him as if she were sure that he would understand and answer her.

The robin did answer. He twittered and chirped and hopped along the wall, as if he were telling her all sorts of things. It seemed to Mistress Mary as if she understood him, too, though he was not speaking in words. It was as if he said:

"Good morning! Isn't the wind nice? Isn't the sun nice? Isn't everything nice? Let us both chirp and hop and twitter. Come on! Come on!"

Mary began to laugh, and as he hopped and took little flights along the wall she ran after him. Poor little thin, sallow, ugly Mary – she actually looked almost pretty for a moment.

"I like you! I like you!" she cried out, pattering down the walk; and she chirped and tried to whistle, which last she did not know how to do in the least. But the robin seemed to be quite satisfied and chirped and whistled back at her. At last he spread his wings and made a darting flight to the top of a tree, where he perched and sang loudly.

That reminded Mary of the first time she had seen him. He had been swinging on a tree-top then and she had been standing in the orchard. Now she was on the other side of the orchard and standing in the path outside a wall – much lower down – and there was the same tree inside.

"It's in the garden no one can go into," she said to herself. "It's the garden without a door."

From *The Secret Garden*
Frances Hodgson Burnett (1849–1924)

Glossary

orchard an area for growing fruit trees, such as apple trees and pear trees
sallow sickly-looking, unhealthy-looking

Part 1

1. In her first speech, what tells us that Mary has seen the robin before?

____ 1 mark

2. Where had she been the first time she saw the robin?

____ 1 mark

3. Write **two** words that the author uses to describe how the robin 'speaks'.

____ 2 marks

4. What does plain-looking Mary do that makes her look 'almost pretty'?

____ 1 mark

5. Which word describes how Mary looks – pale and unhealthy?

____ 1 mark

Part 2

6. What does Mary try to do, but doesn't know how to do?

____ 1 mark

7. Why does Mary describe the garden as 'the garden no one can go into'?

____ 1 mark

8. Why is it easy for the robin to go into the secret garden?

____ 1 mark

9. What do you think Mary might do next, after the end of this extract? Explain why you think this.

____

____

____ 3 marks

page 15
total out of 12

Written in March

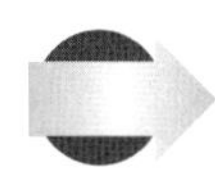

This classic poem was written over 100 years ago, but includes many scenes that are still familiar to us today. It describes the change from one season to another, in the month of March.

The cock is crowing.
The stream is flowing.
The small birds twitter.
The lake doth glitter.
The green field sleeps in the sun.

The oldest and youngest
Are at work with the strongest.
The cattle are grazing,
Their heads never raising.
There are forty feeding like one!

Like an army defeated
The snow hath retreated
And now doth fare ill.
On the top of the bare hill,
The plough-boy is whooping –
anon – anon.

There's joy in the mountains.
There's life in the fountains.
Small clouds are sailing.
Blue sky prevailing.
The rain is over and gone.

William Wordsworth (1770–1850)

Part 1

1. The poet lived a long time ago. The language he uses is old-fashioned. For example, he writes 'doth (does) glitter' (verse 1), when we would say 'is glittering'.

   Replace the underlined word below with the word we would use today.

   The snow hath (________) retreated. — 1 mark

2. The poet says that the cattle never raise their heads. Why do you think this is?

   ____ — 1 mark

3. What does the poet say the snow is like as it moves away?

   ____ — 1 mark

4. Which season do you think the poem describes? Explain how you know.

   ____

   ____ — 2 marks

Part 2

5. Is the setting of this poem rural (in the countryside) or urban (in the town)? Quote **two** lines that show this.

   ____

   ____ — 3 marks

6. a) What is the mood of the poem? (ring **two**)

   worried angry happy sleepy optimistic — 2 marks

   b) Quote **two** lines from the poem that made you choose these words.

   ____

   ____ — 2 marks

page 17
total out of 12

Measuring straight lines

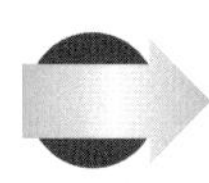

To measure things we need suitable units. People need to agree standards for these so that everybody uses the same scale. This text explains the history of measurements, from Ancient Egypt to the present day.

Have you ever mislaid your ruler or helped someone to look for a missing tape-measure? In days gone by you could never lose your tape-measure or ruler, as all the units of measure were parts of your body. The width of a man's thumb was called an **inch**. The length of his foot was, unsurprisingly, called a **foot**. The distance from a man's nose to the tip of his outstretched arm was known as a **yard**. These units fit neatly together: twelve inches equal one foot. Three feet equal one yard.

We were not the first to use parts of our bodies as units of measure. In Ancient Egypt, a builder's ruler was attached to him. The width of his finger was a **digit**. This was useful for measuring small lengths. Then there was the width of his hand, a unit called a **palm**. The distance from the tip of his elbow to the tip of his middle finger was called a **cubit**. These units fit neatly together, too: four digits equal one palm; seven palms equal one cubit.

There was one problem with using an arm as a unit of measure: not everyone is the same size. If a tailor with long arms bought cloth from a merchant with short arms, they would sometimes argue about who should measure out the material. There was only one way to stop fights in the marketplace. The government ordered the use of standard measures with standard units.

Today, most countries use the standard **metric system**. This is how it was devised. If you imagine drawing a line on the surface of the earth that passed through the north and south poles, that would be called a **meridian**. Break that line into four equal parts, and you have one quarter of a meridian, which is called a **quadrant**. Now imagine breaking a quadrant into ten million equal parts. The length of *one* of these parts is called a **metre**: the standard unit of the metric system. The metre can then be broken into smaller units – the **centimetre**, which is one hundredth of a metre, and the **millimetre**, which is one thousandth of a metre.

Glossary

merchant someone who buys and sells things
tailor someone who makes clothes, especially coats and suits

Part 1

1. Explain **one** advantage (a good point) of using a part of your body as a measuring stick, instead of a ruler.

______________________________ 1 mark

2. Which of these measures is longer:

a) a foot or a yard? ______________________________ 1 mark

b) a cubit or a digit? ______________________________ 1 mark

3. Which part of the body was used to measure one inch?

______________________________ 1 mark

4. If you were buying a yard of material before the days of standard units, would you prefer the merchant to be tall or short? Explain why.

____

______________________________ 2 marks

Part 2

5. In Ancient Egyptian units of measure, how many digits equal one palm?

______________________________ 1 mark

6. How many palms measure the same as one cubit? ______________ 1 mark

7. Write the missing word to complete the sentence.

The measuring system that is based on the measurements of the earth is called the ______________ system. 1 mark

8. How many centimetres are there in one metre? ______________ 1 mark

9. Which Ancient Egyptian measure would you use to work out the length of:

a) your bed? (ring **one**) digit palm cubit 1 mark

b) a caterpillar? (ring **one**) digit palm cubit 1 mark

page 19
total out of 12

Bird meets chimpanzee

This text comes from a story called *The Beak Speaks*. At the beginning of this episode, a chimpanzee has arrived by falling down the chimney, taking a mynah bird by surprise.

The soot got up my beak. I sneezed so hard I did a reverse spin on my perch and fell off. I felt so undignified, lying there with my legs waving in the air. I struggled back on to my perch and tried to look nonchalant, but interesting.

The chimpanzee just sat in the fireplace, holding out his left arm and gazing at it intently.

"I've broken my arm," he said mournfully. "Look."

He lifted it a little and the front half hung down. He pushed it with his other hand and it swung from one side to the other.

"You see? It's broken there, right in the middle."

"That's your elbow," I said.

His head jerked up and he looked at me with such joy. "Really? Do you really think so? It's not broken?"

"It's definitely your elbow," I said, and I was thinking, This chimp's an idiot.

Almost as if he wanted to prove my point, the chimp now lifted his right arm and made that one swing backwards and forwards, too. He was delighted.

"Look! Look! The other one does the same thing! I've got *two* elbows!"

"Congratulations," I muttered, while the chimp sat in the fireplace making both arms swing at once and blissfully beaming at them.

I shall let you into a secret. I have often sat in my cage, all alone, and wondered, Wouldn't it be nice if I had a companion? Someone I could talk with. We could muse upon the state of the world. We could chat about fashion and how to get the glossiest feathers and how to strut with style. What fun that would be! It was a lovely, comforting kind of thought.

And who do I get to talk to? A chimpanzee with a brain problem – the problem being that he didn't seem to have one.

From *The Beak Speaks*
Jeremy Strong

Glossary

companion someone to talk to or play with, someone who spends time with you
intently with great attention, without being distracted
nonchalant (French: non-shall-unt) unconcerned, as if not bothered, not caring

Part 1

1. Which character is telling the story, using the word 'I'? ______________ 1 mark

2. a) What does the bird have instead of a nose? ______________ 1 mark

   b) What makes the bird sneeze? ______________ 1 mark

3. The word 'chimp' is short for what longer word?

   ______________ 1 mark

4. What is the bird's opinion of the chimp? Do you agree? Explain why.

   ____

   ______________ 2 marks

Part 2

5. When the chimp thinks he has broken his arm, he speaks 'mournfully'. What does this tell us about how he feels?

   ______________ 1 mark

6. What shows us that the chimp is surprised that his arm is not broken?

   ______________ 2 marks

7. a) Give **one** example of when you might say 'Congratulations!' to someone.

   ______________ 1 mark

   b) Why is it funny to congratulate the chimp on having two elbows?

   ______________ 1 mark

8. If the bird had a friend to chat to, what would she like to talk about?

   ______________ 1 mark

page 21
total out of 12

Get the picture?

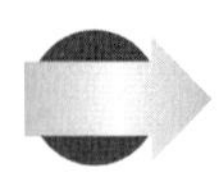

The title of this poem is a play on words. 'Get the picture?' means 'Can you imagine the scene?' It also reflects the events in the poem, as the narrator (the speaker) shows some holiday photographs to a friend.

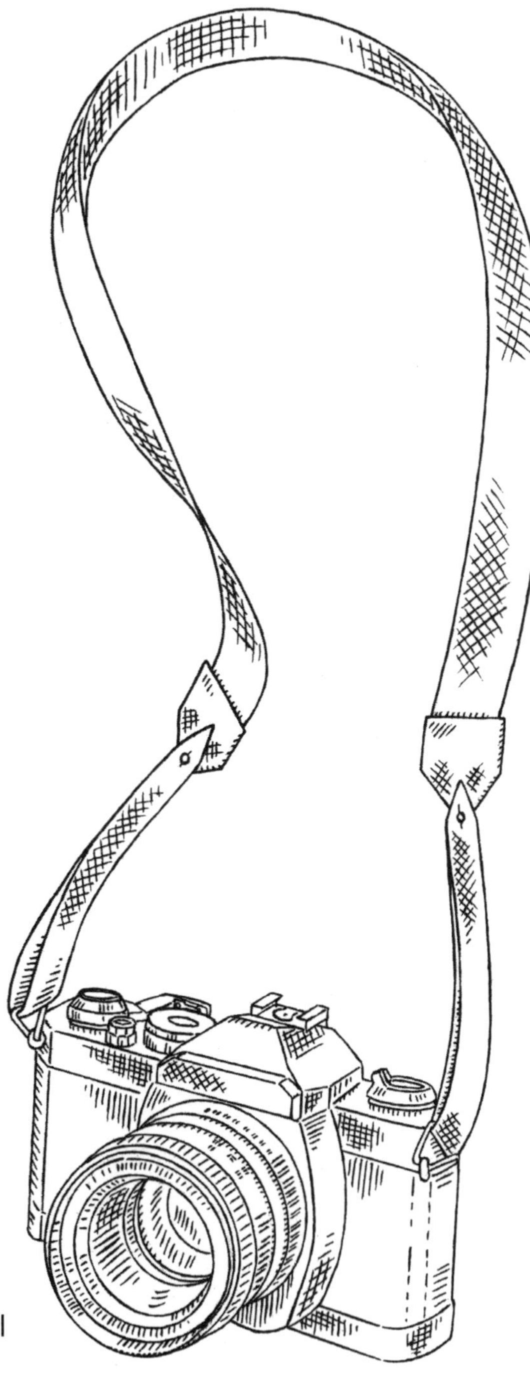

This is us at breakfast our first morning
And this one's Dad – he's carrying his tray.
This is David half asleep – he's yawning –
And this one's after breakfast on our way.

Here we are all posing by the seashore
And this is Mum – she's reading in the shade.
Here's someone we met – his name was Trevor –
And that's our castle – that's me with the spade.

Here's us, later, eating at a diner
And here's Belinda in a Stetson hat.
That's one of a passing ocean liner –
Yes, it's a little blurred – a shame is that.

Here we are that evening having dinner
And here we're doing line dancing in rows,
That boy there – small world – he lives in Pinner
And here's Dad standing on some lady's toes.

We've a whole lot more if you are staying
And please do say if you are getting bored,
Pardon me – I missed what you were saying,
Oh, you weren't saying anything – you snored!

Philip Waddell

Glossary

Stetson hat a type of cowboy hat

Part 1

1. The speaker describes each photo. Sometimes they describe things that you can see in the photo. At other times, they give extra information.

   Find these lines in the poem and tick the correct box for each one.

Tick one box only for each statement	in photo	extra information
a) 'he's yawning'		
b) 'his name was Trevor'		
c) 'that's me with the spade'		

3 marks

2. Where has the speaker been on holiday? ______________________ 1 mark

3. Does the speaker live near Pinner? How do you know?

   ____ 1 mark

4. If David is related to the speaker, what relation is he most likely to be?

   ____ 1 mark

Part 2

5. Which photograph is out of focus?

   ____ 1 mark

6. Who is most interested in the holiday photos – the speaker or the friend? Explain why you think this.

   ____

   ____ 2 marks

7. Write captions below these pictures, based on information in the poem.

3 marks

______________ ______________ ______________

______________ ______________ ______________

page 23
total out of 12

Figurative expressions

All the headwords in this text begin with the letter R. They are arranged in alphabetical order, like a dictionary of figurative expressions. These are sayings that people use in everyday conversation.

rain *it never rains but it pours* – one piece of bad luck is just the start of more

rat *like a drowned rat* – soaking wet
to smell a rat – to suspect something

record *to break the record* – to achieve more than anyone before, especially in sports

red *red flag* – a warning of danger
to be caught red-handed – to be seen in the middle of wrong-doing
red-letter day – a memorable or important day

rein *to give free rein to* – to allow a person to have his or her own way
to take the reins – to take control; to take charge of events

Rome* *Rome wasn't built in a day* – it takes time to complete any worthwhile task

rope *to give someone plenty of rope* – to let people behave as they wish, hoping that they might make a mistake
to know the ropes – to be very familiar with a job or activity

rough *to rough it* – to put up with discomfort and hardship
rough and ready – hastily prepared, without neatness or decoration
rough and tumble – in a disorderly manner

**Rome, capital city of Italy, was once the capital city of the huge Roman Empire, whose power and influence took many battles and many years to grow.*

Part 1

1. Which saying suggests that when one thing goes wrong, more bad luck follows? ______________________ 1 mark

2. If you let someone do what they want, you give them free __________. 1 mark

3. Which word is linked with both danger and importance?

______________________ 1 mark

4. If you ran faster than anyone else, what would you break?

______________________ 1 mark

5. **Two** of the key words listed are 'homophones'. (They sound the same but have different spellings and meanings.) What are these **two** words?

______________________ 2 marks

Part 2

6. If you 'know the ropes' you are (ring **one**):

   experienced   an adult   a climber   used to danger. 1 mark

7. Choose suitable expressions from the text to complete these sentences.

   a) The police saw the man stealing gold rings. The man was . . .

   ______________________ 1 mark

   b) I ran to school in the pouring rain and arrived looking like . . .

   ______________________ 1 mark

8. Where would this entry fit into the list on page 24? Fill in the missing words.

   ride   *to take someone for a ride* – to cheat or deceive someone

   a) It should appear after __________ and before __________.

   b) Why it would fit there? ______________________

   ______________________ 3 marks

page 25
total out of 12

Tracy Beaker's nightmare

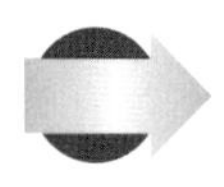

Tracy Beaker is living in a children's home because her foster parents, Julie and Ted, decided that they could not look after her as they are having a baby of their own. 'Aunty Peggy' worked at another children's home, where Tracy lived before.

There wasn't much point in getting to sleep, because when I did eventually nod off I just had these stupid nightmares. It's as if there's a video inside my head and it switches itself on the minute my eyes close and I keep hoping it's going to be showing this great comedy that'll have me in stitches but then the creepy music starts and I know I'm in for it. Last night was the Great Horror Movie of all time. I was stuck in the dark somewhere and there was something really scary coming up quick behind me so I had to run like mad. Then I got to this big round pool and there were these stepping stones with people perching on them and I jumped on to the first one and there was no room at all because that fat Aunty Peggy was spread all over it. I tried to cling to her but she gave me a big smack and sent me flying. So then I jumped on to the next stepping stone and Julie and Ted were there and I tried to grab hold of them but they just turned their backs on me and didn't even try to catch me when I fell and so I had to try to reach the next stepping stone but I was in the water doing my doggy-paddle and it was getting harder and harder, and every time I swam to a stepping stone all these people prodded at me with sticks and pushed me away and I kept going under the water and . . .

. . . and then I woke up ...

Jacqueline Wilson

Glossary

foster parents adults who provide a safe place for a child to be cared for

Part 1

1. How does Tracy know that the 'video' in her head is not going to be a comedy?

____ 1 mark

2. Tracy talks about what happens as if it is a video, but what is it really?

____ 1 mark

3. What is coming up behind Tracy that scares her? (ring **one**)

a monster   she doesn't see what it is   Aunty Peggy   1 mark

4. How does Tracy describe the way she swims?

____ 1 mark

Part 2

5. Use the explanations in the green box to write the meaning of each phrase on the lines below.

laughing hard   knocked me over   going to be in trouble   fall asleep

nod off ______________________________

in stitches ______________________________

in for it ______________________________

sent me flying ______________________________ 4 marks

6. How do you think Tracy feels when she wakes up? Explain your answer

____

____ 2 marks

page 27
total out of 10

from **Roadways**

John Masefield loved the sea and it features in many of his poems. Often, as here, he expresses a longing to be at sea instead of on dry land.

One road leads to London,
One road leads to Wales,
My road leads me seawards
To the white dipping sails.

One road leads to the river,
As it goes singing slow;
My road leads to shipping,
Where the bronzed sailors go.

Leads me, lures me, calls me
To salt, green, tossing sea;
A road without earth's road-dust
Is the right road for me.

A wet road, heaving, shining,
And wild with seagulls' cries,
A mad salt sea-wind blowing
The salt spray in my eyes.

From *Roadways*
John Masefield (1878–1967)

Part 1

1. Which **two** words show that the speaker is in Great Britain?

______________________________ 2 marks

2. a) What are the white sails in the first verse?

____

b) What makes the sails look as if they are 'dipping'?

______________________________ 2 marks

3. Which of these words could you use to describe sailors who are 'bronzed'? (ring **one**)

sun-tanned   wealthy   contented   tired out   1 mark

4. What does the sea seem to be doing to the poet?

______________________________ 1 mark

Part 2

5. As the poet thinks of the sea, what colour does he imagine it?

______________________________ 1 mark

6. What is the 'wet road' in the last verse?

______________________________ 1 mark

7. Imagine you are standing on the deck of a ship at sea. Reread the last verse. Name **two** sounds you might hear.

____

______________________________ 2 marks

page 29
total out of 10

Early bicycles

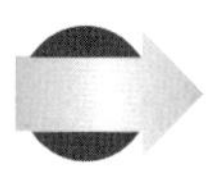

Most people learn to ride a bike when they are children. People say it is a skill that no-one ever forgets. The bicycles we know today are very different from the early models described in this text.

Cycling is fun, healthy and a good way to travel to school or work. It's also a very popular hobby – whether you prefer BMX racing, mountain biking or just cycling round the park.

The first recognisable bicycle was the 'hobby horse'. It was invented in Germany in 1817 and had a wooden frame, wooden wheels and no pedals. Riders had to push along with their feet in order to move. This made some people describe it as a 'walking machine'.

Over twenty years later, in 1839, a Scottish blacksmith called Kirkpatrick Macmillan fitted footrests to the front wheel of his hobby horse. The bike was heavy, but more practical than the original hobby horse – especially going downhill.

In 1861, a bicycle with steering was invented – the French velocipede. The seat was put on a spring to make the cyclist more comfortable, but it did not help very much and the bike became known as the 'boneshaker'.

The 'penny-farthing' was invented in 1870. Unlike earlier bikes, the penny-farthing's wheels were made of steel instead of wood and had solid rubber tyres. The front wheel was much larger than the back wheel, just as the old British penny coin was much larger than the old farthing coin.

The 'safety bicycle' replaced the penny-farthing and became the bike we know today. Just like the modern bicycle, the safety bicycle had chain-driven pedals. Harry Lawson's 1873 model was one of the best, with better brakes, pneumatic tyres, ball-bearings, and the ability to 'free-wheel'.

Glossary

ball-bearings small metal balls that reduce friction (rubbing) between two metals; used on a bike to help the pedals turn easily
blacksmith someone who makes things out of metal, often to do with horses
pneumatic tyre a rubber tyre filled with air

Part 1

1. Fill in the missing words to finish the sentences below:

   The ____________ was the name of the first bicycle.

   It was made of ____________. 2 marks

2. The blacksmith, Kirkpatrick Macmillan, lived and worked in (ring **one**):

   England Scotland Wales Ireland. 1 mark

3. a) What was the proper name of the bicycle that was nicknamed the 'boneshaker'?

   ______________________________ 1 mark

   b) Explain why the 'boneshaker' might have earned its nickname.

   ______________________________ 1 mark

Part 2

4. Describe the wheels of a penny-farthing bike as fully as you can. (What did they look like? What were they made of?) 2 marks

   ____

   ____

5. a) In which year was Lawson's bicycle produced?

   ______________________________ 1 mark

   b) Name **one** thing that Lawson's bicycle had and which modern bikes have too.

   ______________________________ 1 mark

6. What is inside a pneumatic tyre?

   ______________________________ 1 mark

page 31
total out of 10

A strange dream

When Mary Poppins arrives to look after Jane and Michael, the children soon discover that she is no ordinary nanny (childminder). Even after knowing her for some time, they are still not sure of just how magical she is.

"I had such a strange dream last night," said Jane, as she sprinkled sugar over her porridge at breakfast. "I dreamed we were at the Zoo and it was Mary Poppins's birthday, and instead of animals in the cages there were human beings, and all the animals were outside –"

"Why, that's *my* dream. I dreamed that, too," said Michael, looking very surprised.

"We can't both have dreamed the same thing," said Jane. "Are you sure? Do you remember the Lion who curled his mane and the Seal who wanted us to –"

"Dive for orange-peel?" said Michael. "Of course I do! And the babies inside the cage, and the Penguin who couldn't find a rhyme –"

"Then it couldn't have been a dream at all," said Jane **emphatically**. "It must have been *true*. And if it was –" She looked curiously at Mary Poppins, who was boiling milk.

"Mary Poppins," she said, "could Michael and I have dreamed the same dream?"

"You and your dreams!" said Mary Poppins, sniffing. "Eat your porridge, please, or you will have no buttered toast."

But Jane would not be put off. She *had* to know.

"Mary Poppins," she said, looking very hard at her, "were you at the Zoo last night?"

Mary Poppins's mouth opened widely.

"At the Zoo? Me at the Zoo – at night? *Me*? A quiet, orderly person who knows what is what, *and* what isn't –"

"But *were* you?" Jane persisted.

"Certainly not – the idea!" said Mary Poppins. "And I'll thank you to eat up your porridge and no nonsense."

Jane poured out her milk.

"Then it must have been a dream," she said, "after all."

From *Mary Poppins*
P.L. Travers (1899–1996)

Glossary

emphatically decidedly, firmly

Part 1

1. At what time of day does this event take place? Explain how you know.

____

____ 2 marks

2. How does the author show that Michael interrupts Jane when she is talking?

____ 1 mark

3. What is Mary Poppins doing while the children discuss their dreams?

____ 1 mark

4. After their porridge, what do the children expect to have next for breakfast?

____ 1 mark

Part 2

5. At first, Mary Poppins avoids answering Jane's questions. How does she do this? Read the list below and tick **two** that you think are true.

a) She changes the subject to talk about breakfast.	
b) She turns her back on Jane and ignores her.	
c) She keeps repeating Jane's question without answering.	
d) She talks to Michael instead.	
e) She tells Jane that it was all a funny dream.	

2 marks

6. What is Mary Poppins' opinion of herself?

She thinks she is _______________________________________ . 2 marks

7. Does Jane believe Mary Poppins when she says, 'Certainly not'? Explain your answer.

____ 1 mark

____

page 33
total out of 10

Riddles of the seashore

Each verse of this poem is a riddle. You need to read the words carefully to puzzle out which sea-creature – or sea-related item – the verse is about.

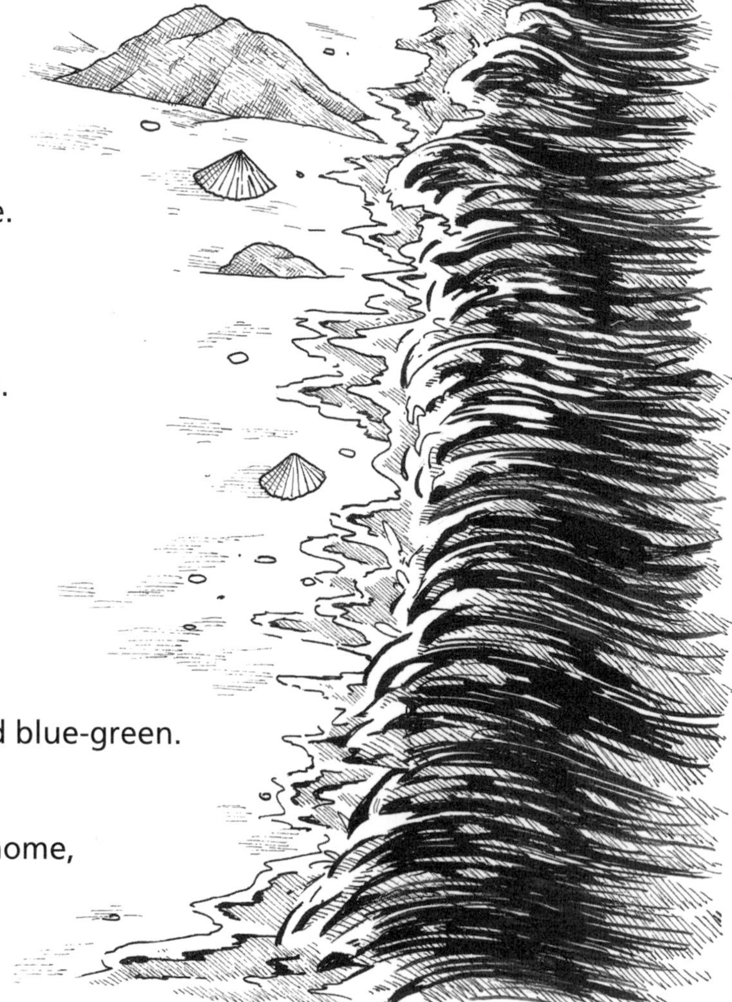

Tossed into tangles by waves
it drizzles salt-sparkle onto sand.

?

Soft under seaweed the toe-nipper
waits for new armour.

?

Pentagram on the beach
fish with a sky-name.

?

Not for collecting or poking,
leave this jellymould body for the tide.

?

In a bowl of barnacled rock a tiny sea
covers sea-flowers, shrimps and a crab.

?

Written in the sand, a seagull's poem
is rubbed out by waves.

?

As far as the eye can see, scallops
of white embroidery on grey-blue and blue-green.

?

Holding secret sea-songs and carried home,
it spills music into my ear.

Catherine Benson

Part 1

1. Read the third verse. A 'pentagram' has five points. What sort of creature has a 'sky-name'? Colour in its picture below. 1 mark

2. a) A young crab sheds its shell as it grows, then waits to grow a new one. Where does it wait, while it is soft and cannot defend itself?

   ______________________________ 1 mark

   b) What word does the poet use to describe its new shell?

   ______________________________ 1 mark

3. a) What is 'tossed into tangles by waves'? (ring **one**)

   feather   sand-fly   shell   seaweed 1 mark

   b) What drips from this on to the sand? ______________ 1 mark

Part 2

4. One verse describes a rock pool. Write the first **three** words of this verse.

   ______________________________ 1 mark

5. a) Which creature waits for the tide to wash it back into the sea?

   ______________________________ 1 mark

   b) Which verse of the poem describes this creature?

   ______________________________ 1 mark

6. What does verse 7 describe?

   ______________________________ 1 mark

7. Have you ever picked up a sea shell and held it to your ear? What does the poet suggest you might hear if you did?

   ______________________________ 1 mark

page 35
total out of 10

Fossil hunting

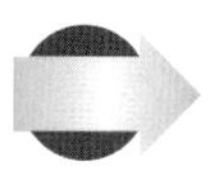

Discover some of the fascinating fossils you can find around Britain, what they look like and where to look for them. They will help you to find out about how life on Earth has changed.

Where can you find fossils?

Search for fossils in sedimentary rocks like mudstone and limestone. These rocks are the best because fossils form when an animal, plant, or other signs of life such as a dinosaur footprint, becomes buried in sediment, which is usually grains of mud or sand. Over thousands of years layers of sediment build up, eventually turning into a sedimentary rock.

You can usually find fossils anywhere that sedimentary rocks are exposed at the surface. Look along the coast on beaches, in quarries, on farm land, or even in your own garden.

Ammonites

Ammonites are related to the squids and octopuses you can see today, but they're all extinct – they died out at the same time as dinosaurs.

Their shell is usually a flat spiral shape. It is made up of chambers, like little rooms within the shell, connected by a tube. The animal only lived in one of these chambers and used the other spaces to help it float. Some ammonites were tiny, others as big as a man.

Because ammonites lived in the sea, if you find an ammonite fossil in a rock, you know that millions of years ago the spot where you're standing used to be totally covered by the ocean.

From the *National History Museum* website, 2013

Fossil hunting can take you to dangerous, rocky areas. Ask an adult to come with you to help you keep safe.

Glossary

fossil the remains or mark of an ancient plant, creature or footprint in rock

sedimentary (of sediment) sand or dirt that is carried by water or wind and deposited onto land

Part 1

1. The title of this article is 'Fossil hunting'. Which sub-title is a question?

____ 1 mark

2. Give **two** examples of places where you might look for fossils.

____

____ 2 marks

3. When creatures die out – as ammonites have – they become (ring **one**):

external extinct extreme expressed. 1 mark

4. a) Ammonites are related to creatures alive today that live in (ring **one**):

the forest the sea rivers fields mountains. 1 mark

b) Name **one** such creature. ___________________________ 1 mark

Part 2

5. Label the ammonite by writing its name below its picture.

__________ __________ __________ __________ 1 mark

6. What size were ammonites? ___________________________

____ 2 marks

7. Choose **one** word of the words below to write on the line.

hundreds thousands millions

Ammonites lived on our planet ________________ of years ago. 1 mark

page 37
total out of 10

Camping with Toad

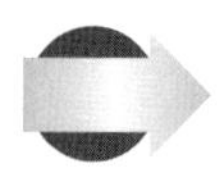

Rat and Mole have gone with their friend Toad on a short holiday in his caravan. They have just stopped travelling for the night and pulled up for a rest and something to eat.

Late in the evening, tired and happy and miles from home, they drew up on a remote common far from habitations, turned the horse loose to graze, and ate their simple supper sitting on the grass by the side of the cart. Toad talked big about all he was going to do in the days to come, while stars grew fuller and larger all around them, and a yellow moon, appearing suddenly and silently from nowhere in particular, came to keep them company and listen to their talk. At last they turned into their little bunks in the cart; and Toad, kicking out his legs, sleepily said, "Well, good night, you fellows! This is the real life for a gentleman! Talk about your old river!"

"I *don't* talk about my river," replied the patient Rat. "You *know* I don't, Toad. But I *think* about it," he added pathetically, in a lower tone. "I think about it – all the time!"

The Mole reached out from under his blanket, felt for the Rat's paw in the darkness, and gave it a squeeze. "I'll do whatever you like, Ratty," he whispered. "Shall we run away tomorrow morning, quite early – *very* early – and go back to our dear old hole on the river?"

"No, no, we'll see it out," whispered back the Rat. "Thanks awfully, but I ought to stick by Toad till this trip is ended. It wouldn't be safe for him to be left to himself. It won't take very long. His fads never do. Good night!"

From *The Wind in the Willows*
Kenneth Grahame (1859–1932)

Glossary

common a piece of grassland that anyone may use, an area freely open to the public
fad craze, fashion, brief interest in something
habitation dwellings, living places, homes of people or creatures
pathetically miserably, in a pitiful way

Part 1

1. What time of day is it when the friends arrive on the common?

____ 1 mark

2. How do they feel when they arrive on the common?

____ 2 marks

3. What does 'graze' mean? (ring **one**):

sleep eat grass rest recover wait 1 mark

4. Which phrase tells us that Toad talks in a boastful way?

____ 1 mark

5. What tells us that Rat is feeling a little homesick?

____ 1 mark

6. What does Mole do that shows he feels sorry for Rat?

____ 1 mark

Part 2

7. When Toad says, "Talk about your old river!" he means (ring **one**):

that he is not impressed by Rat's river

that he wants Rat to tell him about his river. 1 mark

8. Each statement is either 'True' or 'False'. Put a tick in the correct box.

Tick one box only for each statement	True	False
a) It is a mainly clear night.		
b) Mole is cross with Rat.		
c) Toad, Rat and Mole sit on the grass to eat their evening meal.		
d) Rat is responsible and trustworthy.		

4 marks

page 39
total out of 12

Schofield & Sims

the long-established educational publisher specialising in maths, English and science

First Comprehension provides an early introduction to written comprehension, developing children's enthusiasm for reading and their ability to interpret texts. When working through the series, support from an adult will boost children's confidence and help them to understand and evaluate each text. The books are easy to mark and provide a permanent record of each child's work, helping you to monitor progress.

Designed to support the National Curriculum for Years 2 and 3, the content of this series has wide appeal and may also be used by older children.

The series provides:

- a **brief introduction**, enabling teachers, parents and adult helpers to use the books effectively
- passages from **classic and contemporary fiction** to broaden children's reading experience
- a wide selection of **poetry**, from William Wordsworth to Tony Mitton
- stimulating **non-fiction** extracts, with different subjects and structures
- a **range of question types**, including direct, inferential and evaluative questions.

First Comprehension Book 2 is aimed at children who are gaining confidence in written comprehension. It is designed to stretch high achievers in Year 2 (ages 6–7), and also provides extra practice for children in Year 3 (ages 7–8). Eighteen carefully selected texts reflect the range of genres recommended by the National Curriculum, and accompanying questions are presented in two parts, to suit the concentration level of most children in this age group. The second of two **First Comprehension** activity books, this book features work by writers such as Kenneth Grahame and Jacqueline Wilson, as well as an autobiographical text and a number of accessible non-fiction texts.

The separate **Teacher's Guide** contains teaching notes, sample answers and further activities for each text, allowing you to use **First Comprehension** to its full potential.

The full range of books in the series is as follows.

First Comprehension Book 1	ISBN 978 07217 1220 8
First Comprehension Book 2	ISBN 978 07217 1221 5
First Comprehension Teacher's Guide	ISBN 978 07217 1222 2

Key Stage 2 Comprehension is available for older children.

ISBN 978 07217 1221 5
Key Stages 1 & 2
Age range: 6–8 years
£3.95 (Retail price)

For further information and to place your order visit
www.schofieldandsims.co.uk or telephone 01484 607080